Time Tests

Mental Maths

by Norman D Lock
cover illustration by Gary Slater

A catalogue record for this book is available from the British Library

Published by Ladybird Books Ltd
27 Wrights Lane London W8 5TZ
A Penguin Company

2 4 6 8 10 9 7 5 3 1

© LADYBIRD BOOKS LTD MM

text © Norman D Lock MCMXCV

Test 1

1	16
2	50% of this
3	n^2
4	six extra
5	x 4
6	10% of this
7	$\frac{1}{7}$ of this
8	multiply by nine
9	$\sqrt{n}$
10	x 8

What is your answer?

Check your answer at the back of the book.

Record your time on the Record Sheet.

Test 2

1	£5
2	20% of this
3	x 23
4	deduct £2
5	$33\frac{1}{3}$% of this
6	1% of this
7	x 60
8	add on 30p
9	double it
10	30% of this

What is your answer?

Check your answer at the back of the book.

Record your time on the Record Sheet.

Test 3

1	three hundred
2	subtract 30
3	$\div$ 90
4	n^2
5	n^2
6	minus 9
7	$\frac{5}{8}$ of this
8	add on 3
9	$\frac{5}{6}$ of this
10	5% of this

What is your answer?

Check your answer at the back of the book.

Record your time on the Record Sheet.

Test 4

1	£5.50
2	double it
3	times by 3
4	take away 100p
5	75% of this
6	$\frac{3}{8}$ of this
7	half of it
8	10% of this
9	an extra 9p
10	$\div$ 6

What is your answer?

Check your answer at the back of the book.

Record your time on the Record Sheet.

Test 5

1	one thousand
2	25% of this
3	$\frac{1}{2}$ of this
4	less 4
5	$\sqrt{n}$
6	x 8
7	remove 8
8	times by 4
9	5% of this
10	$\sqrt{n}$

What is your answer?

Check your answer at the back of the book.

Record your time on the Record Sheet.

Test 6

1	£4
2	plus 10%
3	add 10p
4	double it
5	x 6
6	deduct £6
7	1% of this
8	$\frac{7}{8}$ of this
9	$\frac{2}{7}$ of this
10	$66\frac{2}{3}\%$ of this

What is your answer?

Check your answer at the back of the book.

Record your time on the Record Sheet.

Adding together larger numbers in your head is easier than you think.

Look at this example:

55 + 19 looks horrible!

55 + 20 is easy... 75

19 is one less than 20, so we can do it like this:

55 + 19 is the same as:
55 + (20 − 1) = 75 − 1
$\qquad\qquad$ = 74

Here is another:

66 + 28

Think of it like this:
66 + (30 − 2) = 96 − 2
$\qquad\qquad$ = 94

And another:

48 + 37
48 + (40 − 3) = 88 − 3
$\qquad\qquad$ = 85

1	26
2	+ 19
3	$\frac{2}{9}$ of this
4	n^2
5	7% of this
6	multiply by 8
7	+ 18
8	subtract 4
9	50% of this
10	$\frac{3}{5}$ of this

What is your answer?

Check your answer at the back of the book.

Record your time on the Record Sheet.

Test 8

1	£20
2	1% of this
3	x 8
4	deduct 10p
5	double it
6	times by 9
7	plus £19
8	subtract £6
9	75% of this
10	25% of this

What is your answer?

Check your answer at the back of the book.

Record your time on the Record Sheet.

Test 9

1	25
2	+ 17
3	+ 19
4	minus one
5	$33\frac{1}{3}$% of this
6	x 9
7	10% of this
8	$\frac{4}{9}$ of this
9	multiply by 50
10	3% of this

What is your answer?

Check your answer at the back of the book.

Record your time on the Record Sheet.

Test 10

1	34p
2	x 100
3	add on £18
4	subtract 400p
5	25% of this
6	10% of this
7	half of it
8	x 5
9	times by 100
10	$\frac{1}{4}$ of this

What is your answer?

Check your answer at the back of the book.

Record your time on the Record Sheet.

Test 11

1	400
2	divide equally into 5 parts
3	20% of this
4	add nine
5	$\sqrt{n}$
6	x 70
7	10% of this
8	$\frac{2}{5}$ of this
9	+ 29
10	+ 18

What is your answer?

Check your answer at the back of the book.

Record your time on the Record Sheet.

Taking away larger numbers in your head is also easier than you think.

Look at this example:

42 – 19

We can do this by first taking away 20 and then adding on 1.

Think of it like this:

42 – 20 (+ 1) = 22 + 1
= 23

Here is another example:

76 – 28

Think of it like this:

76 – 30 (+ 2) = 46 + 2
= 48

And another:

83 – 46
83 – 50 (+ 4) = 33 + 4
= 37

1	37
2	minus nineteen
3	$\frac{2}{3}$ of this
4	double it
5	double it
6	double it
7	take away 18
8	3 extra
9	$\sqrt{n}$
10	$\sqrt{n}$

What is your answer?

Check your answer at the back of the book.

Record your time on the Record Sheet.

Test 13

1	£55
2	deduct £27
3	25% of this
4	x 9
5	subtract £19
6	10% of this
7	$\frac{1}{2}$ of this
8	take away 10p
9	$33\frac{1}{3}\%$ of this
10	multiply by 6

What is your answer?

Check your answer at the back of the book.

Record your time on the Record Sheet.

Test 14

1	seventy three
2	remove 16
3	plus 3
4	60% of this
5	divide by 9
6	n^2
7	+ 19
8	double it
9	80% of this
10	subtract 18

What is your answer?

Check your answer at the back of the book.

Record your time on the Record Sheet.

Test 15

1	six hundred
2	8% of this
3	− 19
4	three more
5	times by 2
6	$\sqrt{n}$
7	x 90
8	10% of this
9	increase by 29
10	take away 100

What is your answer?

Check your answer at the back of the book.

Record your time on the Record Sheet.

Test 16

1	£1.25
2	times by 10
3	double it
4	4% of this
5	x 17
6	+ £38
7	20% of this
8	half of it
9	10% of this
10	deduct 19p

What is your answer?

Check your answer at the back of the book.

Record your time on the Record Sheet.

Now we can look at a way of **multiplying** larger numbers.

Look at this example:

3 x 19

Think of it this way:

3 x 20 then (− 3) = 60 − 3
= 57

You need to take away 3 because, although 19 is only 1 less than 20, you have multiplied this difference of 1 by 3.

Here is another example:

4 x 18
4 x 20 then (− 8) = 80 − 8
= 72

The difference between 20 and 18 is 2. Multiply this by 4, and you need to take away another 8.

And some more:

5 x 39
5 x 40 (− 5) = 200 − 5
= 195

3 x 68
3 x 70 (− 6) = 210 − 6
= 204

1	nineteen
2	times by 4
3	5 extra
4	$\frac{7}{9}$ of this
5	minus 17
6	half of this
7	add 7
8	90% of this
9	$66\frac{2}{3}\%$ of this
10	x 3

What is your answer?

Check your answer at the back of the book.

Record your time on the Record Sheet.

Test 18

1	6p
2	× 100
3	add on 50%
4	multiply by 6
5	1% of this
6	subtract 5p
7	4 lots of this
8	deduct £1
9	half of it
10	25% of this

What is your answer?

Check your answer at the back of the book.

Record your time on the Record Sheet.

Test 19

1	eighty
2	4 times this
3	20% of this
4	add on 39
5	take three
6	$\sqrt{n}$
7	$\frac{3}{5}$ of this
8	× 30
9	20 extra
10	add on 25%

What is your answer?

Check your answer at the back of the book.

Record your time on the Record Sheet.

Test 20

1	£60
2	take away 10%
3	÷ 9
4	7% of this
5	plus 8p
6	times by 100
7	add on 20%
8	half of it
9	half of it
10	half of it

What is your answer?

Check your answer at the back of the book.

Record your time on the Record Sheet.

Test 21

1	thirty eight
2	multiply by 4
3	100 less than this
4	+ 18
5	30% of this
6	$66\frac{2}{3}\%$ of this
7	16 more
8	double it
9	5% of this
10	x 29

What is your answer?

Check your answer at the back of the book.

Record your time on the Record Sheet.

You learnt in *Short cuts to Percentages* that **'per cent'** means **out of a hundred.**

If **50%** means $\frac{50}{100} = \frac{1}{2}$ then

100% means $\frac{100}{100} = 1$ which is the same as **all** of a given amount.

50% of £8 is £4
100% of £8 is £8

200% means **two times** the given amount.

200% of £8 is £16, and
500% of £8 is £40

150% is the same as **one and a half times** the given amount.

150% of £8 is £12

$1\frac{1}{2}$ x 8 = 12 (see *Short cuts to Percentages*)

What do you think 225% means?

Yes, $2\frac{1}{4}$ times the given amount.

225% of £8:

$$2 \times £8 = £16$$
$$\frac{1}{4} \times £8 = \ £2$$
$$225\% \text{ of } £8 = £18$$

1	£40
2	plus 5%
3	share equally among 6 people
4	2% of this
5	+ 19p
6	x 100
7	$66\frac{2}{3}\%$ of this
8	300% of this
9	deduct £10
10	÷ 7

What is your answer?

Check your answer at the back of the book.

Record your time on the Record Sheet.

Test 23

1	thirteen
2	+ 39
3	remove 2
4	150% of this
5	minus 11
6	$\sqrt{n}$
7	x 29
8	subtract 200
9	125% of this
10	40% of this

What is your answer?

Check your answer at the back of the book.

Record your time on the Record Sheet.

Test 24

1	£7
2	1000% of this
3	half of this
4	10% of this
5	less £1.50
6	250% of this
7	x 18
8	6% of this
9	plus 60p
10	150% of this

What is your answer?

Check your answer at the back of the book.

Record your time on the Record Sheet.

Test 25

1	£59
2	x 3
3	£5 less than this
4	10% of this
5	add 80p
6	$\frac{5}{6}$ of this
7	200% of this
8	9% of this
9	multiply by 10
10	$\frac{2}{3}$ of this

What is your answer?

Check your answer at the back of the book.

Record your time on the Record Sheet.

Test 26

1	£50
2	less 10%
3	$\frac{7}{9}$ of this
4	plus £25
5	350% of this
6	$\frac{4}{7}$ of this
7	25% of this
8	half of it
9	half of it
10	half of it

What is your answer?

Check your answer at the back of the book.

Record your time on the Record Sheet.

To find 15% is easy.

Calculate 10%, then halve it to find 5% and add the two together to give you 15%.

Look at this example:

Find 15% of £40:

$$10\% = £4$$
$$5\% = £2$$
$$\overline{15\% = £6}$$

Find 15% of £8:

$$10\% = £0.80$$
$$5\% = £0.40$$
$$\overline{15\% = £1.20}$$

To find $17\frac{1}{2}\%$ we take things one stage further. Halve 5% to give you $2\frac{1}{2}\%$.

So, $17\frac{1}{2}\%$ of £20 is

$$10\% = £2.00$$
$$5\% = £1.00$$
$$2\frac{1}{2}\% = £0.50$$
$$\overline{17\frac{1}{2}\% = £3.50}$$

Find $17\frac{1}{2}\%$ of £60:

$$10\% = £6.00$$
$$5\% = £3.00$$
$$2\frac{1}{2}\% = £1.50$$
$$\overline{17\frac{1}{2}\% = £10.50}$$

1	£8
2	600% of this
3	£2 more
4	15% of this
5	double it
6	$\frac{4}{5}$ of this
7	X 3
8	£19 less than this
9	add £3
10	$17\frac{1}{2}\%$ of this

What is your answer?

Check your answer at the back of the book.

Record your time on the Record Sheet.

Test 28

1	9
2	n^2
3	decrease by 1
4	$17\frac{1}{2}\%$ of this
5	$\frac{3}{7}$ of this
6	x 19
7	take 100
8	times by 5
9	70% of this
10	multiply by 3

What is your answer?

Check your answer at the back of the book.

Record your time on the Record Sheet.

Test 29

1	£90
2	15% of this
3	take away £7
4	200% of this
5	x 3
6	£21 more
7	$\frac{3}{4}$ of this
8	$33\frac{1}{3}\%$ of this
9	$\frac{1}{2}$ of this
10	20% of this

What is your answer?

Check your answer at the back of the book.

Record your time on the Record Sheet.

Test 30

1	77
2	decrease by 28
3	$\sqrt{n}$
4	ten lots of this
5	150% of this
6	25 fewer than this
7	$17\frac{1}{2}\%$ of this
8	x 2
9	125% of this
10	$\frac{6}{7}$ of this

Test 31

1	3p
2	x 200
3	times by 9
4	take away £18
5	double it
6	÷ 8
7	3% of this
8	x 100
9	another £3
10	15% of this

If $\frac{1}{4} = 25\%$
then $\frac{1}{8}$ must be $12\frac{1}{2}\%$
because $\frac{1}{8}$ is half of $\frac{1}{4}$.

$\frac{3}{8}$ will be	$\frac{1}{4}\left(\text{or } \frac{2}{8}\right) + \frac{1}{8}$
or $37\frac{1}{2}\% =$	$25\% + 12\frac{1}{2}\%$

$\frac{5}{8}$ will be	$\frac{1}{2}\left(\text{or } \frac{4}{8}\right) + \frac{1}{8}$
or $62\frac{1}{2}\% =$	$50\% + 12\frac{1}{2}\%$

$\frac{7}{8}$ will be	$\frac{3}{4}\left(\text{or } \frac{6}{8}\right) + \frac{1}{8}$
or $87\frac{1}{2}\% =$	$75\% + 12\frac{1}{2}\%$

Learn these off by heart:

$\frac{1}{8} = 12\frac{1}{2}\%$

$\frac{1}{4}\left(\frac{2}{8}\right) = 25\%$

$\frac{3}{8} = 37\frac{1}{2}\%$

$\frac{1}{2}\left(\frac{4}{8}\right) = 50\%$

$\frac{5}{8} = 62\frac{1}{2}\%$

$\frac{3}{4}\left(\frac{6}{8}\right) = 75\%$

$\frac{7}{8} = 87\frac{1}{2}\%$

$1\left(\frac{8}{8}\right) = 100\%$

1	£67
2	remove £19
3	$12\frac{1}{2}\%$ of this
4	x 20
5	add on 50%
6	5% of this
7	multiply by 7
8	£17 more
9	15% of this
10	4% of this

What is your answer?

Check your answer at the back of the book.

Record your time on the Record Sheet.

Test 33

1	one hundred
2	take 28
3	$37\frac{1}{2}\%$ of this
4	+ 3
5	4 times this
6	$17\frac{1}{2}\%$ of this
7	$\frac{5}{7}$ of this
8	add on $33\frac{1}{3}\%$
9	120% of this
10	$37\frac{1}{2}\%$ of this

What is your answer?

Check your answer at the back of the book.

Record your time on the Record Sheet.

Test 34

1	£560
2	$12\frac{1}{2}\%$ of this
3	plus 10%
4	£29 less than this
5	$62\frac{1}{2}\%$ of this
6	plus 25%
7	add on £2.50
8	$62\frac{1}{2}\%$ of this
9	half of it
10	half of it

What is your answer?

Check your answer at the back of the book.

Record your time on the Record Sheet.

Test 35

1	twelve
2	n^2
3	increase by 6
4	50% of this
5	subtract 11
6	$87\frac{1}{2}\%$ of this
7	24 more
8	add on 15%
9	4 fewer than this
10	add on $12\frac{1}{2}\%$

What is your answer?

Check your answer at the back of the book.

Record your time on the Record Sheet.

Test 36

1	18p
2	x 100
3	double it
4	$\frac{5}{6}$ of this
5	plus 10%
6	deduct £9
7	$62\frac{1}{2}\%$ of this
8	$66\frac{2}{3}\%$ of this
9	times by 8
10	plus $2\frac{1}{2}\%$

What is your answer?

Check your answer at the back of the book.

Record your time on the Record Sheet.

How do we find out what...

6 is $\frac{1}{2}$ (50%) of?

$\frac{1}{2}$	$\frac{1}{2}$
6	6

6 is $\frac{1}{2}$ (50%) of 12

5 is $\frac{1}{4}$ (25%) of?

$\frac{1}{4}$	$\frac{1}{4}$	$\frac{1}{4}$	$\frac{1}{4}$
5	5	5	5

5 is $\frac{1}{4}$ (25%) of 20

Those were easy. What about these?

14 is $\frac{2}{3}$ (66$\frac{2}{3}$%) of?

If 14 is $\frac{2}{3}$, then 7 must be $\frac{1}{3}$,

$\frac{1}{3}$	$\frac{1}{3}$	$\frac{1}{3}$
7	7	7

$\underbrace{\qquad}_{\frac{2}{3}}$

Here we have to split 14 to fit into **two** of the one third boxes.

This means putting 7 in each box.

Now we can see that:

14 is $\frac{2}{3}$ (66$\frac{2}{3}$%) of 21

Look at these other examples:

12 is $\frac{3}{4}$ (75%) of?

$\frac{1}{4}$	$\frac{1}{4}$	$\frac{1}{4}$	$\frac{1}{4}$
4	4	4	4

$\underbrace{\qquad\qquad}_{\frac{3}{4}}$

12 is $\frac{3}{4}$ (75%) of 16

18 is $\frac{3}{5}$ (60%) of?

$\frac{1}{5}$	$\frac{1}{5}$	$\frac{1}{5}$	$\frac{1}{5}$	$\frac{1}{5}$
6	6	6	6	6

$\underbrace{\qquad\qquad}_{\frac{3}{5}}$

18 is $\frac{3}{5}$ (60%) of 30

1	forty seven
2	decrease by 39
3	this is $\frac{1}{3}$ of the next number
4	$\frac{5}{8}$ of this
5	double it
6	110% of this
7	this is 50% of the next number
8	plus 6
9	12$\frac{1}{2}$% of this
10	$\sqrt{n}$

What is your answer?

Check your answer at the back of the book.

Record your time on the Record Sheet.

Test 38

1	£16
2	this is $\frac{2}{3}$ of the next amount
3	+ £6
4	this is 75% of the next amount
5	250% of this
6	less £19
7	$\frac{5}{9}$ of this
8	2% of this
9	x 6
10	50% of this

What is your answer?

Check your answer at the back of the book.

Record your time on the Record Sheet.

Test 39

1	£200
2	$17\frac{1}{2}$% of this
3	remove £11
4	this is $37\frac{1}{2}$% of the next amount
5	200% of this
6	deduct £100
7	this is $\frac{4}{5}$ of the next amount
8	double it
9	4% of this
10	x 2

What is your answer?

Check your answer at the back of the book.

Record your time on the Record Sheet.

Test 40

1	280
2	÷ 70
3	n^2
4	+ 19
5	this is $\frac{5}{8}$ of the next number
6	7 more
7	$\frac{2}{9}$ of this
8	x 3
9	add 102
10	$\sqrt{n}$

What is your answer?

Check your answer at the back of the book.

Record your time on the Record Sheet.

Test 41

1	£39
2	x 5
3	minus £45
4	this is $\frac{3}{4}$ of the next number
5	8% of this
6	+ £4
7	this is 80% of the next amount
8	$\frac{2}{5}$ of this
9	1% of this
10	times by 99

What is your answer?

Check your answer at the back of the book.

Record your time on the Record Sheet.

Test 42

1	£8
2	plus 25%
3	x 7
4	less 10%
5	divide by 7
6	5% of this
7	add on 3p
8	this is $\frac{2}{3}$ of the next amount
9	x 100
10	25% of this

What is your answer?

Check your answer at the back of the book.

Record your time on the Record Sheet.

Test 43

1	83
2	− 29
3	$\frac{5}{6}$ of this
4	$\frac{2}{9}$ of this
5	less 20%
6	x 50
7	20 extra
8	share equally among 7
9	this is 75% of the next number
10	x 9

What is your answer?

Check your answer at the back of the book.

Record your time on the Record Sheet.

Test 44

1	£5
2	6% of this
3	x 8
4	200% of this
5	subtract 30p
6	400% of this
7	multiply by 5
8	plus 10%
9	$\frac{4}{9}$ of this
10	this is $\frac{2}{3}$ of the answer

What is your answer?

Check your answer at the back of the book.

Record your time on the Record Sheet.

Test 45

1	1000
2	25% of this
3	less 10%
4	$\sqrt{n}$
5	$66\frac{2}{3}$% of this
6	x 48
7	200 less than this
8	75% of this
9	10% of this
10	this is $\frac{3}{5}$ of the answer

What is your answer?

Check your answer at the back of the book.

Record your time on the Record Sheet.

Test 46

1	£25
2	plus 10%
3	less £1.50
4	double it
5	deduct £4
6	2% of this
7	$33\frac{1}{3}\%$ of this
8	subtract 2p
9	this is 30% of the next amount
10	x 234

What is your answer?

Check your answer at the back of the book.

Record your time on the Record Sheet.

Test 47

1	two hundred
2	less 2%
3	$\sqrt{n}$
4	150% of this
5	x 3
6	÷ 9
7	n^2
8	200% of this
9	increase by 2
10	this is 10% of the answer

What is your answer?

Check your answer at the back of the book.

Record your time on the Record Sheet.

Record Sheet

Date	Test No.	Time	Score

Record Sheet

Date	Test No.	Time	Score

Record Sheet

Date	Test No.	Time	Score

Record Sheet

Date	Test No.	Time	Score